Key Stage 2

# Decimals & Percentages

Hilary Koll and Steve Mills

Name _____

Schofield & Sims

# Introduction

Decimals and percentages are both just different ways to write fractions (which are parts of things). A half is the same as 0.5 and also 50 per cent. When working with units of measurement you usually use decimals, and when looking at problems with large numbers you may find percentages more useful. In this book you will find information about how to write and use decimals and percentages. You will practise working with them, and learn when and how to use them.

## How to use this book

Before you start using this book, write your name in the name box on the first page.

Then decide how to begin. If you want a complete course on decimals and percentages, you should work right through the book from beginning to end. Another way to use the book is to dip into it when you want to find out about a particular topic, such as comparing decimals. The Contents page will help you to find the pages you need.

Whichever way you choose, don't try to do too much at once – it's better to work through the book in short bursts.

When you have found the topic you want to study, look out for the icons below which mark different parts of the text.

This icon shows you the activities that you should complete. You write your answers in the spaces provided. You might find it useful to have some spare paper to work on for some of the activities. After you have worked through all the activities on the page, turn to pages 45–49 at the end of the book to check your answers. When you are sure that you understand the topic, put a tick in the box beside it on the Contents page.

On pages 12, 22, 28 and 35 you will find **Progress tests**. These contain questions that will check your understanding of the topics that you have worked through so far. Check your answers on page 50. It is important that you correct any mistakes before moving on to the next section.

On pages 41–44 you will find a **Final test**. This will check your understanding of all the topics. Check your answers on page 51.

## Explanation

This text explains the topic and gives examples. Make sure you read it before you start the activities.

This text gives you useful background information about the subject.

# Contents

# How decimals are written

## Explanation

Decimals, like fractions, are **part numbers** because they include amounts that are less than **1**, for example **0.3**, **4.68** and **36.782**.

Decimals are easier to use than fractions because they work like whole numbers.

**Whole numbers**

Th  H  T  U . t  h  th

**10** units make **1** ten, **10** tens make **1** hundred, **10** hundreds make **1** thousand and so on.

**Decimals**

Th  H  T  U . t  h  th

**10** thousandths make **1** hundredth, **10** hundredths make **1** tenth, **10** tenths make **1** unit and so on.

When you are working with decimals you need to know what each digit in the number stands for.

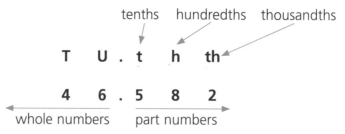

The numbers to the left of the decimal point show how many whole numbers you have.

The numbers to the right show how many tenths, hundredths, thousandths and so on you have.

One-tenth means **1** out of **10**    and is written **0.1**

One-hundredth means **1** out of **100**    and is written **0.01**

So **0.34** means **3** tenths and **4** hundredths or **34** hundredths    and is written **0.34**

Decimals & Percentages

# Decimal tenths and hundredths

The **decimal point** separates whole numbers from part numbers.

**3 9 . 4 2**

whole numbers | part numbers

decimal point

**Tenths**

The first digit to the right of the decimal point is the tenths digit.
This is because **10** tenths make a whole one.

| U | . | t | h |
|---|---|---|---|
| 6 | . | 8 | 5 |

## Activities

**1** Draw a ring around the **tenths** digit in these numbers.

a 2.⑥    b 6.③    c 7.⑨

d 13.⑥    e 28.①    f 56.④

g 8.⑤4    h 9.⑤6    i 23.⑥3

**Hundredths**

The second digit to the right of the decimal point is the hundredths digit.
**10** hundredths make **1** tenth and **100** hundredths make a whole one.

| U | . | t | h |
|---|---|---|---|
| 8 | . | 2 | 7 |

**2** Draw a ring around the **hundredths** digit in these numbers.

a 2.7②    b 5.4③    c 9.0②

d 27.5①    e 65.9⑦    f 128.4⑥

g 5.4⑨2    h 8.0⑦2    i 19.6⑧8

**3** What is the **green** digit worth in each of these numbers?

a **2.56**  _6 hundredths_    b **18.42** 4 _Tenth_    c **38.97** 9 _Tenth_

d **156.64** 4 _hundreth_    e **280.85** 8 _tenth_    f **56.841** 4 _Hundreth_

# Writing decimals

## Explanation

Decimals are types of fractions with a denominator (bottom number) of **10**, **100** or **1000** and so on.

- One-tenth can be written as the fraction $\frac{1}{10}$ or as the decimal **0.1**.

- One-hundredth can be written as the fraction $\frac{1}{100}$ or as the decimal **0.01**.

As you saw on page 4, a decimal such as **0.34** is actually the same as **3** tenths and **4** hundredths, or **34** hundredths. It is the same as the fraction $\frac{34}{100}$.

## Activities

**1**  Write each description as a decimal.

a  four-tenths        $\frac{4}{10}$

b  eight-tenths        $\frac{9}{10}$

c  three-hundredths        $\frac{3}{100}$

d  six-hundredths        $\frac{6}{100}$

e  twenty-two-hundredths        $\frac{22}{60} \frac{}{100}$

f  ninety-six-hundredths        $\frac{96}{100}$

**2**  Write each fraction as a decimal.

a  $\frac{7}{10}$      0.7

b  $\frac{5}{10}$      0.5

c  $\frac{2}{100}$      2.02

d  $\frac{9}{100}$      0.09

e  $\frac{47}{100}$      0.47

f  $\frac{75}{100}$      0.15

## Did you know?

Decimals and fractions are like two different languages. Different languages mean we can say the same thing in different ways.

French people and Greek people say 'Good morning' in different ways, but they mean the same thing.

**Bonjour**

**Kalimera!**

# Dividing whole numbers by 10 and 100

## Explanation

**Dividing whole numbers by 10**

When something is divided by **10** it is easy to write the answer.

**Example** If **3** cakes are shared among **10** people, each cake is split into tenths and each person is given a slice from each cake. This means that each person will get three-tenths of a cake.

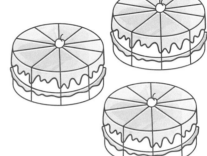

$3 \div 10 = 0.3$

When dividing by **10** the digits of the number move **one** place to the right.

```
 U . t  h                T  U . t  h              H  T  U . t  h
 3 .        ÷ 10          2  7 .        ÷ 10       4  6  8 .        ÷ 10
 0 . 3                       2 . 7                    4  6 . 8
```

## Activities

**1**  Divide each number by **10** and write the answer as a decimal.

**a**    $6 \div 10 =$ _____

**b**    $8 \div 10 =$ _____

**c**   $13 \div 10 =$ _____

**d**   $65 \div 10 =$ _____

**e**  $164 \div 10 =$ _____

**f**  $732 \div 10 =$ _____

---

**Dividing whole numbers by 100**

When dividing by **100** the digits of the number move **two** places to the right.

```
 U . t  h                T  U . t  h              H  T  U . t  h
 3 .        ÷ 100        2  7 .        ÷ 100      4  6  8 .        ÷ 100
 0 . 0  3                  0 . 2  7                  4 . 6  8
```

**2**  Divide each number by **100** and write the answer as a decimal.

**a**    $3 \div 100 =$ _____

**b**    $9 \div 100 =$ _____

**c**   $43 \div 100 =$ _____

**d**   $75 \div 100 =$ _____

**e**  $683 \div 100 =$ _____

**f**  $708 \div 100 =$ _____

**3**  Answer these, giving your answers as decimals.

**a**  $503 \div 10 =$ _____

**b**  $261 \div 100 =$ _____

**c**   $43 \div 10 =$ _____

**d**    $8 \div 100 =$ _____

# Decimals on a number line 1

## Explanation

Whole numbers can be marked on a number line like this:

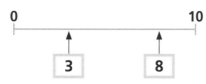

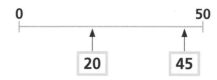

You can do the same with decimals.

This packet of sweets holds **10** sweets.

This picture shows **1.8** packets of sweets.
This means **1** whole packet and **8** tenths of a packet.

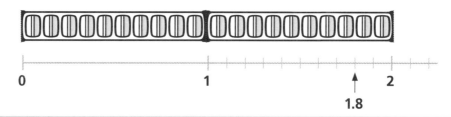

## Activities

**1** Mark how many packets of sweets are shown below.

**a**

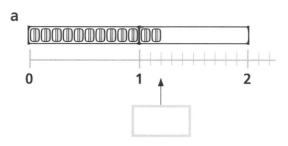

**b**

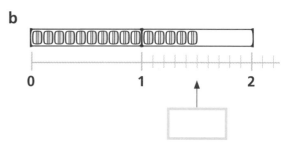

**c**

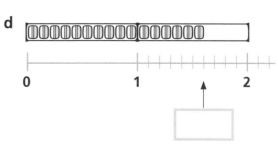

**d**

**2** Mark these numbers with arrows on the number lines.

**a** **1.6, 1.1, 0.7, 0.2**

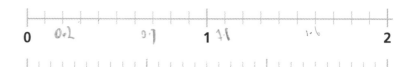

**b** **1.4, 2.4, 0.9, 1.8**

**c** **3.5, 4.3, 4.8, 5.6**

# Rounding decimals 1

## Explanation

Decimals are rounded in the same way as whole numbers.

**Example** Round **7.3** to the nearest whole number.

One way of rounding is to look at the number on a number line and see which whole number it is nearest to.

| 7 | 7.3 | | 8 |

Here is another way.

- First see what you are rounding to.
  'Round 7.3 **to the nearest whole number**.'

- Then look at this digit within the number in the question.
  U . t  h
  7 . **3**

- Now look at the digit to the right of it.
  U . t  h
  7 . 3

- If it is smaller than **5**, the units digit stays the same. If it is **5** or larger, the units digit must go up. **7.3** rounded to the nearest whole number is **7**.

**5 is in the middle. What do you do?**

Round numbers like **3.5**, **4.5** and **9.5** up to the next whole number.

### Did you know?

There are two main reasons for rounding numbers.
- to give a good idea of a number: *there were about **50 000** people at the football match*
- to give a rough answer before calculating:
  **23 × 18** *is about*
  **20 × 20 = 400**

7.3 is nearest to 7.

## Activities

**1** Round these numbers to the nearest **whole number**.

a  3.7 → 4
b  4.3 → 4
c  5.8 → 6

d  7.5 → 8
e  10.5 → 11
f  9.2 → 9

g  18.9 → 19
h  26.4 → 26
i  73.8 → 74

j  132.5 → 133
k  439.4 → 439
l  301.6 → 302

# Comparing decimals 1

It is important to realise that tenths are **larger** than hundredths, hundredths are **larger** than thousandths, and so on.

 **0.7** is larger than **0.07**

## Activities

1 Compare these decimals. Circle the larger decimal in each pair.

a (0.4)   0.04            b 0.07   (0.7)

c 0.08   (0.8)            d (0.5)   0.05

e 0.09   (0.9)            f (0.3)   0.03

2 Compare the decimals in each pair. Write < or > between them.

a 0.1 < 0.5              b 0.03 > 0.02

c 0.08 > 0.04            d 0.7 < 0.9

e 0.12 > 0.09            f 2.04 > 1.04

g 0.78 < 0.87            h 8.7 > 7.8

i 4.75 > 4.25            j 8.78 > 8.69

k 5.18 < 5.81            l 6.43 > 6.34

3 Write the numbers in the bags to make the scales tilt correctly.

a **2.6**kg, **2.8**kg        b **3.75**kg, **3.57**kg        c **5.12**kg, **5.21**kg

Decimals & Percentages

# Ordering decimals 1

## Activities

**1**  Put these decimals in order, starting with the **smallest**.

a  0.6, 0.5, 0.8, 0.3  _____

b  0.07, 0.03, 0.01, 0.08  _____

c  0.53, 0.49, 0.25, 0.83  _____

d  0.82, 0.38, 0.28, 0.83  _____

e  0.09, 0.62, 0.70, 0.11  _____

f  0.13, 0.10, 0.31, 0.03  _____

**2**  Write these in order of size, **largest** first.

a  **0.24**kg, **0.42**kg, **0.30**kg, **0.4**kg

b  **4.5**m, **5.6**m, **5.9**m, **6.0**m

c  **£0.59, £0.50, £5.90, £9.50**

# Progress test 1

**1** Draw a ring around the **tenths** digit in these numbers.

    **a** 7.6          **b** 3.38          **c** 17.95          **d** 24.025

**2** Draw a ring around the **hundredths** digit in these numbers.

    **a** 4.76          **b** 154.73          **c** 94.712          **d** 20.024

**3** What is the green digit worth in each of these numbers?

    **a** 4.59 _____          **b** 24.43 _____          **c** 78.216 _____

**4** Write answers as decimals.

    **a** $53 \div 10 =$ _____      **b** $8 \div 100 =$ _____      **c** $42 \div 100 =$ _____

**5** Write < or > between each pair.

    **a** 0.06 ____ 0.6      **b** 0.4 ____ 0.3      **c** 0.65 ____ 0.56

**6** Put these decimals in order, starting with the **smallest**.

    **a** 0.6, 0.3, 0.1, 0.9      ☐   ☐   ☐   ☐

    **b** 0.75, 0.57, 0.05, 0.77      ☐   ☐   ☐   ☐

**7** Mark these numbers with arrows on the number lines.

    **a** 1.8, 1.3, 0.9, 0.4

                  0                 1                 2

    **b** 0.7, 2.1, 1.9, 1.3

                  0                 1                 2                 3

**8** Round these numbers to the nearest **whole number**.

    **a** 3.6 → ☐      **b** 73.5 → ☐      **c** 29.4 → ☐

Decimals & Percentages

# Decimals on a number line 2

## Explanation

On page 8 you learnt how to mark decimals with tenths on a number line. The line below shows the tenths between the whole numbers **0** and **1**. If you split the line from **0** to **1** into **100** parts you can mark on decimals with hundredths. See how the first part of the number line has been enlarged below to show the hundredths between **0** and **0.1**.

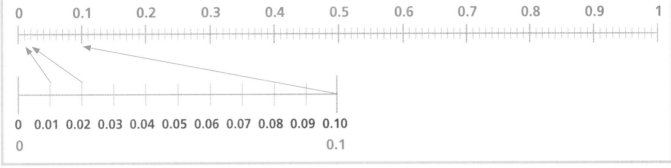

## Activities

**1** Mark these decimals with arrows on the number lines.

**a  0.05, 0.07**

**b  0.45, 0.49**

**c  0.82, 0.86**

**2** Write the decimal each arrow is pointing to.

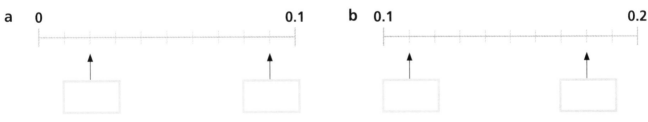

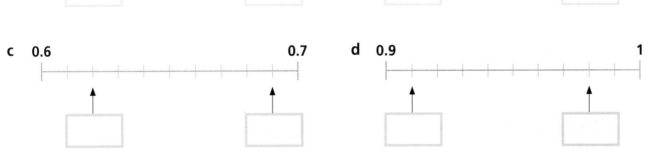

# Rounding decimals 2

## Explanation

Now that you can mark decimals with hundredths on a number line, you can round them to the nearest whole number. Think of the decimals between **0** and **1**, such as **0.01**, **0.32**, **0.49**, **0.67** and **0.81**. Which of them are closer to **0** and which are closer to **1**? The decimals less than **0.5** (half) round down to **0** and those that are **0.5** or greater round up to **1**.

It is similar for decimals that lie between other whole numbers. Look at the tenths digit to help you decide. If it is **5** or higher, it will round up. If it is less than **5**, it will round down.

**Example** Round **5.39** to the nearest whole number. Will **5.39** round down to **5** or up to **6**?

The tenths digit is **3**, so **5.39** will round down to the whole number **5**.

## Activities

1   Round these decimals to the nearest **whole number**.

   a   0.27  →  ☐            b   0.71  →  ☐

   c   5.61  →  ☐            d   5.38  →  ☐

   e   8.42  →  ☐            f   8.51  →  ☐

   g   6.61  →  ☐            h   4.09  →  ☐

   i   9.50  →  ☐            j   15.47  →  ☐

2   Circle the decimals that round to the number **7** (when rounded to the nearest whole number).

   7.09        5.77        6.49        7.65        6.72        6.50

3   Circle the decimals that round to the number **10** (when rounded to the nearest whole number).

   8.99        9.53        10.62        10.43        9.61        10.71

Decimals & Percentages

# Comparing decimals 2

## Explanation

It is important to know that decimal numbers with more digits after the decimal point are not always larger.

**Example**

 **0.7** is larger than **0.68**

Think of this as **0.70** where the zero shows it has no hundredths. It is easier to compare **0.70** with **0.68** as they have the same number of digits after the decimal point.

This number has **two** digits after the decimal point but it does not mean it has to be larger. Always see how many tenths it has.

**Did you know?**

Writing a zero on the end of any decimal doesn't change it at all. **0.5** is the same as **0.50**, and **0.46** is the same as **0.460**. This is a useful thing to know when comparing and ordering decimals.

## Activities

**1** Draw a ring around the larger number in each pair.

**a** 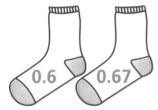 0.6  0.67

**b**  0.5  0.48

**c** 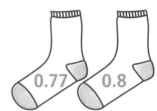 0.77  0.8

**d** 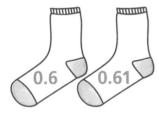 0.6  0.61

**e** 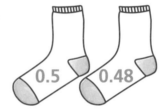 0.72  0.7

**f**  0.9  0.89

**2** Write the numbers in the bags to make the scales tilt correctly.

**a** **0.26**kg, **0.3**kg

**b** **0.5**kg, **0.58**kg

**c** **2.78**kg, **2.8**kg

**d** **4.8**kg, **4.79**kg

**e** **6.05**kg, **6.1**kg

**f** **7.2**kg, **7.18**kg

# Ordering decimals 2

## Explanation

As you learnt on page 11, ordering decimals is just like ordering whole numbers. Start by comparing the digit on the left and, if they are the same, move to the right to compare the next digit.

**Example** Put these decimals in order of size, largest **first**: **0.61, 0.53, 0.7, 0.54**

Which number has most **tenths**?          → **0.7**

Which has the next greatest number of **tenths**?     → **0.61**

Which numbers have the next greatest number of **tenths**?   → **0.53** or **0.54**

Which of these has most **hundredths**?     → **0.54**

Which is the smallest number?     → **0.53**

From largest to smallest the order is: **0.7, 0.61, 0.54, 0.53**

## Activities

**1** Put these decimals in order of size, **smallest** first.

   **a**  **0.9, 0.8, 0.85, 0.56**     _____

   **b**  **0.7, 0.75, 0.83, 0.8**     _____

   **c**  **0.38, 0.41, 0.4, 0.39**     _____

   **d**  **1.86, 1.9, 1.8, 1.87**     _____

   **e**  **2.63, 1.98, 2.0, 2.07**     _____

**2** Write these in order of size, **largest** first.

   **a**  **0.31**kg, **0.53**kg, **0.3**kg, **0.4**kg    

   **b**  **4.2**km, **4.25**km, **4.17**km, **4.3**km    

   **c**  **9.03**m, **9.3**m, **9.13**m, **9.2**m    

   **d**  **3.68**kg, **3.7**kg, **3.8**kg, **3.78**kg

Decimals & Percentages

# Rounding decimals 3

## Explanation

Decimals are rounded to the nearest tenth in the same way as they are rounded to the nearest whole number (see pages 9 and 14).

**Example** Round **0.37** to the nearest tenth.

One way of rounding is to look at the number on a number line and see which tenth the number is nearer to.

**0.3**                              **0.37**            **0.4**

**0.37** is nearer to **0.4**.

Here is another way.

- First see what you are rounding to.
  'Round 0.37 **to the nearest tenth**.'

- Then point to this digit in the number.
  **U   t   h**
  **0 . 3   7**

- Now look at the digit to the right of it.
  **0 . 3   7**

- If it is smaller than **5**, the tenths digit stays the same. If it is **5** or larger, the tenths digit must go up one.

**0.37** rounded to the nearest tenth is **0.4**.

## Activities

**1**  Round these numbers to the nearest **tenth**.

a  4.76 → [ ]      b  5.28 → [ ]      c  6.13 → [ ]

d  8.64 → [ ]      e  9.42 → [ ]      f  10.39 → [ ]

g  14.91 → [ ]     h  16.15 → [ ]     i  20.95 → [ ]

**2**  Round these numbers to the nearest whole number and to the nearest tenth.

| | Nearest whole number | Nearest tenth | | | Nearest whole number | Nearest tenth |
|---|---|---|---|---|---|---|
| a  4.83 | 5 | 4.8 | | b  7.49 | | |
| c  12.76 | | | | d  23.41 | | |
| e  27.725 | | | | f  32.85 | | |

# Relating decimals to fractions

## Explanation

This number line shows how common fractions are related to decimals.

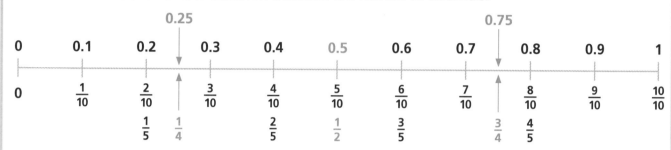

Remember that:

• decimals with one decimal place (one digit after the decimal point) can be written as fractions with the denominator **10**

• decimals with two decimal places (two digits after the decimal point) can be written as fractions with the denominator **100**.

Sometimes those fractions can be simplified: $0.75 = \frac{75}{100} = \frac{3}{4}$

## Activities

**1** Write these decimals as fractions in their simplest form. Use the number line above to help you.

a 0.25 ☐    b 0.4 ☐    c 0.9 ☐    d 0.5 ☐

**2** Can you get across the grid by colouring in **pairs** of touching squares with the same value as each other? Squares can touch at the top, bottom, side or even diagonally.

Start →

| $\frac{1}{6}$ | 0.8 | $\frac{3}{5}$ | 0.5 | $\frac{6}{10}$ | $\frac{1}{10}$ | 0.1 | 0.34 | $\frac{8}{9}$ | 0.1 |
| --- | --- | --- | --- | --- | --- | --- | --- | --- | --- |
| $\frac{1}{2}$ | $\frac{1}{5}$ | $\frac{3}{8}$ | $\frac{4}{5}$ | 0.4 | $\frac{2}{5}$ | 0.73 | $\frac{15}{100}$ | 0.76 | 0.63 |
| $\frac{2}{7}$ | 0.5 | 0.1 | 0.3 | 0.2 | $\frac{2}{3}$ | $\frac{3}{7}$ | 0.15 | $\frac{63}{100}$ | $\frac{8}{9}$ |
| 0.12 | $\frac{1}{4}$ | 0.25 | $\frac{3}{10}$ | $\frac{1}{7}$ | $\frac{87}{100}$ | $\frac{3}{5}$ | 0.75 | 0.11 | 0.2 |

← Finish

# Decimals with a total of one

## Explanation

In the same way that certain pairs of numbers add up to **10** and other pairs have a total of **100**, some pairs of decimals add up to **1**.

Example    $7 + 3 = 10$

$63 + 37 = 100$

$0.64 + 0.36 = 1$

Remember that 10 tenths make one whole or 100 hundredths make one whole.

## Activities

**1** Find pairs of decimals with a total of **1** from the grid and write them below.

| | | | |
|---|---|---|---|
| 0.7 | 0.22 | 0.34 | 0.2 |
| 0.01 | 0.44 | 0.72 | 0.92 |
| 0.9 | 0.17 | 0.39 | 0.78 |
| 0.81 | 0.6 | 0.13 | 0.3 |
| 0.77 | 0.97 | 0.28 | 0.23 |
| 0.66 | 0.51 | 0.11 | 0.38 |
| 0.08 | 0.4 | 0.49 | 0.19 |
| 0.65 | 0.83 | 0.47 | 0.1 |
| 0.02 | 0.8 | 0.99 | 0.35 |

_0.7_ + _0.3_ = 1        _____ + _____ = 1

_____ + _____ = 1        _____ + _____ = 1

_____ + _____ = 1        _____ + _____ = 1

_____ + _____ = 1        _____ + _____ = 1

_____ + _____ = 1        _____ + _____ = 1

_____ + _____ = 1        _____ + _____ = 1

_____ + _____ = 1        _____ + _____ = 1

**2** Find **10** more pairs of decimals with a total of **1** and write them below.

_____ + _____    _____ + _____    _____ + _____    _____ + _____    _____ + _____

_____ + _____    _____ + _____    _____ + _____    _____ + _____    _____ + _____

# Adding and subtracting decimals

## Explanation

You can add decimals in the same way you add whole numbers. Just make sure to line up the decimal points.

When you are adding decimals it is very important to get an approximate answer first. This helps you to be sure that the answer isn't **5.643** or **564.3** instead of **56.43**.

$32.74 + 23.69$

```
  T  U . t  h        (Approx. 30 + 20 = 50)
  3  2 . 7  4
+ 2  3 . 6  9
  5  6 . 4  3
     1    1
```

## Activities

**1**  Add these numbers.

a
```
    1 6 . 7
 +  2 4 . 2
```

b
```
    4 5 . 6
 +  3 8 . 3
```

c
```
    5 2 . 7
 +  3 9 . 8
```

d
```
    4 3 . 5 4
 +  3 7 . 8 3
```

e
```
    1 2 . 8 2
 +      4 . 5 5
```

f
```
    1 2 . 5 3
 +      8 . 4 1
```

g
```
    1 1 . 6 4
 +      8 . 4 2
```

h
```
    8 2 . 3 2
 +  3 5 . 8 8
```

You can subtract decimals in the same way you subtract whole numbers. Just make sure to line up the decimal points.

Check your answer by **adding** the bottom two lines of the calculations, that is **34.72 + 52.78 = 87.50**.

$87.5 - 34.72$

```
  T  U . t  h        (Approx. 90 − 30 = 60)
  8  7 . 5  0
− 3  4 . 7  2
  5  2 . 7  8
```

Fill any blank columns with a **0** to help line them up.

**2**  Subtract these numbers.

a
```
    2 8 . 7
 −  1 4 . 5
```

b
```
    3 6 . 5
 −  1 7 . 3
```

c
```
    7 5 . 6
 −  4 3 . 8
```

d
```
    6 7 . 8 2
 −  4 9 . 3 4
```

e
```
    3 7 8 . 6
 −      9 8 . 7
```

f
```
    2 1 4 . 5
 −  1 8 9 . 4
```

g
```
    1 3 6 . 0 4
 −      6 9 . 7
```

h
```
    1 3 2 . 8
 −      4 9 . 3 4
```

# Word problems

## Explanation

When faced with a problem, follow these steps:

- read the problem carefully
- look for any useful words in the question
- write down any important numbers in the question
- decide what operations to use
- get an approximate answer
- decide whether to use a written or mental method, and work it out
- finally check your answer.

## Activities

1   Solve these money and measurement problems.

a   Sofia has a piece of string that is **5.6**m long. She cuts off a
    length that is **3.9**m long. How much string is left?   _____

b   What is the total length of a line that is **0.8**cm longer than **5.7**cm?   _____

c   Affan cycled **23.6**km in the morning and **6.4**km in the afternoon.
    How far did he cycle altogether?   _____

d   Mr Smith put **0.6**kg of flour, **0.2**kg of butter and **0.3**kg of sugar into
    a bowl to make some biscuits. What is the total mass of the mixture?   _____

e   Hannah had £**17.32**. She bought a magazine costing £**4.85**.
    How much money has she got left?   _____

f   A pan holds **1.2** litres of soup. Luke pours out **0.75** litres of it.
    How much is still in the pan?   _____

g   Sam is **1.65**m tall. His sister is **0.7**m shorter than him.
    How tall is his sister?   _____

h   Rachel has £**14.50** in her purse and £**21.68** in her money box.
    How much more than £**30** does she have?   _____

# Progress test 2

**1** Write the decimal each arrow is pointing to.

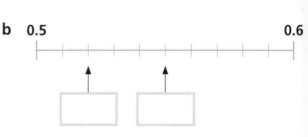

a  0                   0.1     b  0.5                 0.6

**2** Round each decimal to the nearest whole number.

a [ 9.45 ] → [        ]    b [ 6.51 ] → [        ]    c [ 15.38 ] → [        ]

**3** Round each decimal to the nearest tenth.

a [ 0.46 ] → [        ]    b [ 4.53 ] → [        ]    c [ 12.78 ] → [        ]

**4** Draw a ring around the **larger** number in each pair.

a  0.3    0.29        b  0.7    0.79        c  0.9    0.10

**5** Put these decimals in order of size, **smallest** first.

a  0.7, 0.63, 0.59, 0.66                  _____

b  0.1, 0.2, 0.18, 0.81                   _____

c  0.58m, 0.61m, 0.5m, 0.49m     _____

**6** Join pairs of decimals and fractions with the same value.

| $\frac{3}{4}$ | 0.3 | $\frac{4}{5}$ | 0.4 | 0.75 | $\frac{3}{10}$ | 0.8 |
|---|---|---|---|---|---|---|

**7** Answer these questions.

a      2 8 . 7       b      6 7 . 8 2       c     8 1 . 4 5       d     9 3 . 6 7
    + 1 4 . 5            − 1 7 . 3            + 4 3 . 8            − 4 9 . 3

Decimals & Percentages

# Tenths, hundredths and thousandths

## Explanation

### Tenths and hundredths

On page 5, you learnt that the first digit to the right of the decimal point is the **tenths** digit. The second digit to the right of the decimal point is the **hundredths** digit.

| Units | . | tenths | hundredths |
|-------|---|--------|------------|
| 6 | . | 8 | 5 |

## Activities

**1**  Draw a ring round the **tenths** digit and underline the **hundredths** digit in these numbers.

a  3.9̲5

b  4.37

c  8.91

d  0.57

e  15.03

f  38.17

g  78.04

h  10.35

### Thousandths

The third digit to the right of the decimal point is the **thousandths** digit. **10** thousandths make **1** hundredth and **1000** thousandths make a whole one.

| Units | . | tenths | hundredths | thousandths |
|-------|---|--------|------------|-------------|
| 6 | . | 4 | 5 | 7 |

**2**  Draw a ring around the **thousandths** digit in these numbers.

a  3.456

b  5.803

c  11.069

d  8.123

e  35.5091

f  2.9007

g  18.4623

h  2015.2345

**3**  Colour the box that shows the value of the underlined digit.

| | | | | | |
|---|---|---|---|---|---|
| a  8.35̲6 | 50 | 5.0 | 0.5 | 0.05 | 0.005 |
| b  6.9̲03 | 90 | 9.0 | 0.9 | 0.09 | 0.009 |
| c  9.51̲8 | 80 | 8.0 | 0.8 | 0.08 | 0.008 |
| d  12.7̲04 | 70 | 7.0 | 0.7 | 0.07 | 0.007 |
| e  23.82̲6 | 60 | 6.0 | 0.6 | 0.06 | 0.006 |

# Ordering decimals 3

## Explanation

Page 16 explained how to order decimals with up to two digits after the decimal point. The example below shows how to order decimals with more than two digits after the point.

Put these decimals in order of size, largest **first**: **0.783, 0.88, 0.78, 0.9, 0.792**

| | |
|---|---|
| Which number has most **tenths**? $\longrightarrow$ | **0.9** |
| Which has the next greatest number of **tenths**? $\longrightarrow$ | **0.88** |
| Which numbers have the next greatest number of **tenths**? $\longrightarrow$ | **0.783, 0.78** or **0.792** |
| Which of these has most **hundredths**? $\longrightarrow$ | **0.792** |
| Which numbers have the next greatest number of **hundredths**? $\longrightarrow$ | **0.783** or **0.78** |
| Which of these has more **thousandths**? $\longrightarrow$ | **0.783** |
| Which is the smallest number? $\longrightarrow$ | **0.78** |

From largest to smallest the order is: **0.9, 0.88, 0.792, 0.783, 0.78**

## Activities

**1** Put these decimals in order of size, **smallest** first.

  a  **0.7, 0.24, 0.31, 0.86, 0.5**  _____

  b  **0.6, 0.65, 0.594, 0.72, 0.693**  _____

  c  **3.72, 3.278, 3.691, 3.3, 3.467**  _____

  d  **7.063, 7.6, 6.756, 6.007, 7.1**  _____

**2** Write these in order of size, **largest** first.

  a  **£6.07, £6.70, 660**p, **£6.50**

  b  **5.683**kg, **6.58**kg, **6.85**kg, **8.52**kg

  c  **0.348**m, **0.3**m, **0.45**m, **0.42**m

  d  **4.237**m, **4.273**m, **4.732**m, **4.73**m

**3** Use these cards to make as many different numbers as you can. Write your numbers in order, **smallest** first.

  **6**   **3**   **4**   **.**   **0**

  _____

Decimals & Percentages

# Problems involving thousandths

When solving word problems with addition and subtraction of thousandths, just work in the same way as you would with whole numbers.

**Example** What is the total mass of a parcel weighing **0.462**kg and one weighing **0.57**kg?

```
  0 . 4  6  2        Line up the digits correctly and add (or subtract) in the usual way.
+ 0 . 5  7
  1 . 0  3  2        = 1.032kg
      1     1
```

When subtracting, remember to write zeros at the end of the first number if it has fewer digits after the decimal point than the number being subtracted.

**Example** 0.5 − 0.254 = 0.500 − 0.254

## Activities

**1** Solve these measurement problems.

**a** A length of road is **6.352**km long. Katie runs from one end to the other. She stops after **5.265**km. How far does she have still to run? _____

**b** Mrs Khan is fitting a new shelf. She cuts the new shelf from a plank that is **2.016**m long. The shelf is **1.65**m. How long is the part that is left? _____

**c** A baby boy weighed **3.208**kg at birth. He now weighs **4.5**kg. By how much has his weight increased? _____

**d** Harry adds **0.06**kg of fruit jellies and **0.025**kg of marshmallows to a pick and mix bag weighing **0.073**kg. What is the total mass of the bag of sweets? _____

**e** Lena uses **0.725**l of orange juice, **0.5**l of mango juice and **0.95**l of apple juice to make a drink. How much did she make? _____

**f** A bottle holds **0.95**l of washing liquid. Jamie pours out **0.275**l of it. How much is still in the bottle? _____

**g** How much heavier is a box weighing **2.5**kg than one that weighs **2.289**kg? _____

# What percentages are

The symbol that means 'per cent' is %, for example, **100**%, **35**% and **2**%. These are read as 'one hundred per cent', 'thirty-five per cent' and 'two per cent'.

A percentage is a fraction with a **denominator**, or bottom number, of **100**, but it is written in a different way. **Example 36**% means $\frac{36}{100}$.

**100**% means the whole thing. For example, the label on a shirt or T-shirt might say '**100**% cotton', which means it is all cotton.

### Did you know?

**Per cent** means 'out of a hundred'.
**Per** means 'each' or 'every' and **cent** is a Roman word that means 'a hundred'.

Think about **cent**imetre (**100**cm in a metre), **cent** (**100** cents in a Euro), **cent**ipede (they have **100** legs) and **cent**ury (**100** years).

## Activities

**1**  Complete these clothing labels, making sure they make a total of **100**%.

a
**50**% cotton
_____ nylon

b
**20**% cotton
_____ silk

c
_____ cotton
**60**% wool

d
**40**% wool
_____ nylon
**30**% silk

e
**45**% polyester
**15**% cotton
_____ nylon

f
**75**% wool
_____ nylon
**10**% cotton

**2**  Explain what each poster means.

a
"We will be giving **100**%," says player.

b
This yoghurt is **90**% fat free

c
**50**% OFF ALL CDs

_____

_____

_____

# Estimating percentages

Making an estimate is like having a good guess at something. For example, frequently a weather forecaster estimates how likely it is to be rainy or sunny. She might say, "There's a 60% chance of rain today".

Don't worry that your estimates will be wrong. The weather forecast doesn't have to be exactly right – it is just an estimate to give people some idea of what to expect.

## Activities

**1** Match each container with an appropriate estimate.

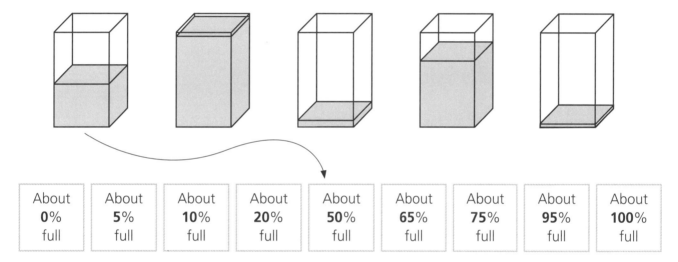

| About 0% full | About 5% full | About 10% full | About 20% full | About 50% full | About 65% full | About 75% full | About 95% full | About 100% full |
|---|---|---|---|---|---|---|---|---|

**2** Match each shape with an appropriate estimate.

| About 0% shaded | About 10% shaded | About 20% shaded | About 35% shaded | About 50% shaded | About 65% shaded | About 75% shaded | About 80% shaded | About 100% shaded |
|---|---|---|---|---|---|---|---|---|

**3** Estimate the percentage of each shape that is shaded.

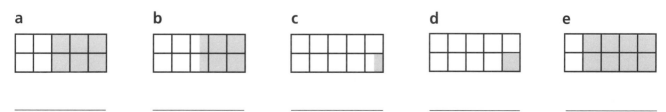

a _____  b _____  c _____  d _____  e _____

**1**  Draw a ring around the **thousandths** digit in these numbers.

a 8.459          b 31.437          c 12.0298          d 1024.4581

**2**  Write the following decimals in digits.

a  zero units, four-tenths and three-thousandths          _____

b  one unit, two-hundredths and nine-thousandths          _____

**3**  Put these decimals in order, starting with the **smallest**.

a  0.045, 0.405, 0.05, 0.4          _____

b  0.032, 0.03, 0.04, 0.008          _____

c  3.573, 3.58, 3.6, 3.59          _____

**4**  Solve this measurement problem.

A window is **1.239**m wide. Ellie wants to put a blind over the window. It must
be **0.013**m wider than the window. What should the width of the blind be?          _____

**5**  Complete these food labels, making sure they total **100**%.

a

50% oranges
_____ lemons

b

65% beans
5%  salt
_____ tomatoes

c

55% potatoes
_____ cheese
10% water

**6**  Match each container with an appropriate estimate.

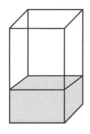 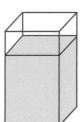 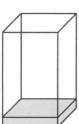 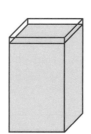 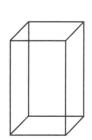

| About 0% full | About 5% full | About 10% full | About 30% full | About 50% full | About 65% full | About 75% full | About 95% full | About 100% full |
|---|---|---|---|---|---|---|---|---|

Decimals & Percentages

# Finding percentages mentally 1

## Explanation

There are several ways to find a percentage of a number or amount.

**To find 50%:** halve the number
50% of 400 → **half** of 400 = 200
50% of £360 → **half** of £360 = £180

**To find 25%:** halve the number and then halve the answer
25% of 400 → **half** of 400 = 200 → **half** of 200 = 100
25% of £360 → **half** of £360 = £180 → **half** of £180 = £90

**To find 75%:** halve the number and halve the answer, then add your two answers together
75% of 400 → **half** of 400 = 200 → **half** of 200 = 100 → 200 + 100 = 300
75% of £360 → **half** of £360 = £180 → **half** of £180 = £90 → £180 + £90 = £270

**Did you know?**
50% is $\frac{1}{2}$
25% is $\frac{1}{4}$
75% is $\frac{3}{4}$

## Activities

**1** Find **50**% of:

a 18 → [ ]
b 24 → [ ]
c 30 → [ ]
d 72 → [ ]

e 96 → [ ]
f 150 → [ ]
g 600 → [ ]
h 1200 → [ ]

**2** Find **25**% of:

a 8 → [ ]
b 16 → [ ]
c 80 → [ ]
d 48 → [ ]

e 60 → [ ]
f 100 → [ ]
g 200 → [ ]
h 880 → [ ]

**3** Find **75**% of:

a 4 → [ ]
b 12 → [ ]
c 48 → [ ]
d 64 → [ ]

e 52 → [ ]
f 160 → [ ]
g 360 → [ ]
h 1000 → [ ]

# Finding percentages mentally 2

## Explanation

To find other percentages in your head you can use **10%**.

**To find 10%:** divide the number by 10
10% of 400 → 400 ÷ **10** = 40
10% of £360 → £360 ÷ **10** = £36

**To find 20%:** divide by 10 and multiply by 2
20% of 400 → 400 ÷ **10** = 40 → 40 × **2** = 80
20% of £360 → £360 ÷ **10** = £36 → £36 × **2** = £72

**To find 30%:** divide by 10 and multiply by 3
30% of 400 → 400 ÷ **10** = 40 → 40 × **3** = 120
30% of £360 → £360 ÷ **10** = £36 → £36 × **3** = £108

You can use this method for **all percentages that are multiples of 10**.

**Example** To find **15%**, first find **10%** and halve your answer to get **5%** then add the two answers together. **15% of 60 = 6 + 3 = 9**

## Activities

1. Find **10%** of:

   a £160 → [ ]   b 280g → [ ]   c 1680m → [ ]

2. Find **40%** of:

   a £80 → [ ]   b 250kg → [ ]   c 900m → [ ]

3. Find **60%** of:

   a £70 → [ ]   b 800km → [ ]   c 120cm → [ ]

4. Find **15%** of:

   a £60 → [ ]   b 180km → [ ]   c 200cm → [ ]

5. Find **35%** of:

   a £400 → [ ]   b 20km → [ ]   c 500cm → [ ]

Decimals & Percentages

# Relating percentages to decimals and fractions 1

## Explanation

The 'Did you know?' fact on page 6 explained that decimals and fractions are like two different languages – two different ways of saying the same thing. Percentages are like a third language, that is another way of saying the same thing.

| | | |
|---|---|---|
| **Percentages** | It is **50**% full. | |
| **Fractions** | It is $\frac{1}{2}$ full. | |
| **Decimals** | It is **0.5** full. | |

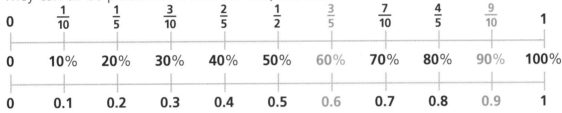

This container can be described in percentages, fractions and decimals.

Percentages, fractions and decimals like these all have the same value.

**Example 60**%, $\frac{3}{5}$ and **0.6**     **90**%, $\frac{9}{10}$ and **0.9**

They can all be placed on a number line, like this:

| 0 | $\frac{1}{10}$ | $\frac{1}{5}$ | $\frac{3}{10}$ | $\frac{2}{5}$ | $\frac{1}{2}$ | $\frac{3}{5}$ | $\frac{7}{10}$ | $\frac{4}{5}$ | $\frac{9}{10}$ | 1 |
|---|---|---|---|---|---|---|---|---|---|---|
| 0 | 10% | 20% | 30% | 40% | 50% | 60% | 70% | 80% | 90% | 100% |
| 0 | 0.1 | 0.2 | 0.3 | 0.4 | 0.5 | 0.6 | 0.7 | 0.8 | 0.9 | 1 |

## Activities

**1** Use the number lines to help you to complete this table. Write the fractions in their simplest form.

| Percentage | Decimal | Fraction |
|---|---|---|
| 50% | | |
| 40% | | |
| | 0.1 | |
| | 0.6 | |
| | | $\frac{7}{10}$ |

| Percentage | Decimal | Fraction |
|---|---|---|
| 80% | | |
| | 0.3 | |
| | | $\frac{1}{5}$ |
| | 0.9 | |
| | 0.01 | $\frac{1}{100}$ |

**2** Draw a ring around the odd one out in each set.

a  25%     0.25     $\frac{2}{5}$          b  75%     0.75     $\frac{7}{5}$

c  40%     0.25     $\frac{2}{5}$          d  90%     0.95     $\frac{9}{10}$

# Relating percentages to decimals and fractions 2

## Explanation

**Converting percentages to decimals and vice versa**

To change percentages into decimals **divide by 100**.    $48\% \rightarrow 48 \div 100 = 0.48$

To change decimals into percentages **multiply by 100**.    $0.3 \rightarrow 0.3 \times 100 = 30\%$

## Activities

**1** Change these percentages into decimals.

a 32% → ☐    b 27% → ☐    c 63% → ☐

d 9% → ☐    e 1% → ☐    f 100% → ☐

**2** Change these decimals into percentages.

a 0.72 → ☐    b 0.45 → ☐    c 0.87 → ☐

d 0.3 → ☐    e 0.6 → ☐    f 0.02 → ☐

**Converting percentages to fractions and vice versa**

To change percentages into fractions, write the percentage as a fraction with a denominator of **100**. Then divide the numerator and denominator by the same number to find the simplest form:

$$48\% = \frac{48 \div 4}{100 \div 4} = \frac{12}{25}$$

To change fractions into percentages, convert $\frac{17}{20}$ into a fraction with a denominator of **100**:

$$\frac{17 \times 5}{20 \times 5} = \frac{85}{100} = 85\%$$

**3** Change these percentages into fractions in their simplest form.

a 49% → ☐    b 15% → ☐    c 84% → ☐

d 5% → ☐    e 1% → ☐    f 75% → ☐

**4** Change these fractions into percentages.

a $\frac{3}{10}$ → ☐    b $\frac{9}{10}$ → ☐    c $\frac{4}{5}$ → ☐

d $\frac{1}{20}$ → ☐    e $\frac{3}{25}$ → ☐    f $\frac{17}{50}$ → ☐

# Percentage problems

## Explanation

Some problems involve writing fractions as percentages, as it is easier to compare percentages than fractions.

**Example** Here are some test scores: $\frac{3}{5}$ $\frac{7}{10}$ $\frac{36}{50}$

Write them as percentages and put them in order, starting with the lowest score.

Look at the number line on page 31 if you need to.

$\frac{3}{5} = 60\%$    $\frac{7}{10} = 70\%$    $\frac{36}{50} = 72\%$    These are in increasing order.

## Activities

**1**  Write these test scores as percentages and then put them in order, starting with the highest.

**a** $\frac{9}{10}$    $\frac{4}{5}$    $\frac{42}{50}$          _____

**b** $\frac{1}{2}$    $\frac{3}{10}$    $\frac{2}{5}$          _____

**c** $\frac{3}{10}$    $\frac{1}{5}$    $\frac{1}{4}$          _____

Some problems involve finding percentages of amounts using the strategies that were used on pages 29 and 30.

**2**  Solve these problems.

**a**  The school hockey team played **15** games. They won **60**% of them.
How many games did they win?          _____

**b**  A school party of **80** children go the London Eye. **40**% of them are girls.
How many are girls?          _____

**c**  **15**% of the children in Year 6 own a cat. If there are **60** children in
Year 6, how many do **not** own a cat?          _____

**d**  How much greater is **75**% of **28** than **90**% of **20**?          _____

# Finding percentages with a calculator

## Explanation

There are different ways to calculate percentages on a calculator because a percentage can be written as either a fraction or a decimal.

**The fraction way**
Think of a percentage as a fraction 'out of **100**' or 'divided by **100**'.
To find **48**% of **56** on a calculator, key in **48**% as a fraction.

$$\frac{48}{100} \times 56 = 26.88 \longleftarrow \text{Key into the calculator } 48 \div 100 \times 56$$

**The decimal way**
Another way is to write each percentage as a decimal.
To find **48**% of **56** on a calculator, key in **48**% as a decimal.

$$0.48 \times 56 = 26.88$$

Use whichever method you prefer, but always approximate first, as below.

**Example** **48**% is a bit less than a half.

$$48\% \text{ of } 56 = 26.88 \longrightarrow \tfrac{1}{2} \text{ of } 60 = 30$$

**26.88** is a bit less than **30** so your answer is likely to be correct.

## Activities

1   Use a calculator to find these percentages. Approximate first.

a  **64**% of **£120** =  _____     b  **32**% of **£48** =  _____

c  **44**% of **£97** =  _____      d  **21**% of **140**kg =  _____

e  **54**% of **224**kg =  _____    f  **23**% of **35**kg =  _____

g  **34**% of **87**ml =  _____     h  **58**% of **250**ml =  _____

i  **41**% of **610**ml =  _____    j  **99**% of **290**m =  _____

k  **36**% of **118**m =  _____     l  **72**% of **184**m =  _____

2   Work out these percentages to find the sale prices. Approximate first.

a   | **45**% of **£21**       b   | **32**% of **£35**       c   | **57**% of **£69**

_____              _____              _____

d   | **23**% of **£60**       e   | **84**% of **£40**       f   | **39**% of **£60**

_____              _____              _____

Decimals & Percentages

# Progress test 4

**1** Find **50**% of:

**a** 48 → ☐          **b** 92 → ☐          **c** 180 → ☐

**2** Find **25**% of:

**a** 24 → ☐          **b** 60 → ☐          **c** 120 → ☐

**3** Find **75**% of:

**a** 8 → ☐          **b** 36 → ☐          **c** 400 → ☐

**4** Find **30**% of:

**a** £200 → ☐          **b** 150kg → ☐          **c** 310m → ☐

**5** Find **45**% of:

**a** £60 → ☐          **b** 200km → ☐          **c** 500cm → ☐

**6** Complete these tables. Write the fractions in their simplest form.

| Percentage | Decimal | Fraction |
|---|---|---|
| 70% | | |
| | 0.4 | |
| | | $\frac{3}{10}$ |

| Percentage | Decimal | Fraction |
|---|---|---|
| 20% | | |
| | 0.5 | |
| | | $\frac{4}{5}$ |

**7** Solve these problems.

**a** Write these test scores as percentages. Which is greater?

$\frac{4}{5}$     $\frac{3}{4}$          _____

**b** A school party of **50** people visits a museum.
**42**% are boys. **8**% are adults. How many are girls?          _____

## Explanation

The Explanation on page 7 described how to divide whole numbers by **10** and **100**.

When dividing by **10** the digits of the number move **one** place to the right.
When dividing by **100** the digits of the number move **two** places to the right.
When dividing by **1000** the digits of the number move **three** places to the right.

| U . t  h  th | | T  U . t  h  th | | H  T  U . t  h  th | |
|---|---|---|---|---|---|
| 3 . | ÷ 1000 | 2  7 . | ÷ 1000 | 4  6  8 . | ÷ 1000 |
| 0 . 0  0  3 | | 0 . 0  2  7 | | 0 . 4  6  8 | |

## Activities

**1**  Write each answer as a decimal.

a  4 ÷   10 = _____      b  29 ÷   10 = _____

c  4 ÷  100 = _____      d  29 ÷  100 = _____

e  4 ÷ 1000 = _____      f  29 ÷ 1000 = _____

Multiplying follows the same pattern, but the digits move to the **left**.

When multiplying by **10** the digits of the number move **one** place to the left.
When multiplying by **100** the digits of the number move **two** places to the left.
When multiplying by **1000** the digits of the number move **three** places to the left.

| U . t  h  th | | T  U . t  h  th | | H  T  U . t  h  th | |
|---|---|---|---|---|---|
| 0 . 0  0  3 | × 1000 | 0 . 0  2  7 | × 1000 | 0 . 4  6  8 | × 1000 |
| 3 . | | 2  7 . | | 4  6  8 . | |

**2**  Write each answer as a decimal.

a  0.06  ×   10 = _____      b  0.006 ×   10 = _____

c  0.07  × 100 = _____      d  0.015 × 100 = _____

e  0.006 × 1000 = _____      f  0.046 × 1000 = _____

g  0.12  ×   10 = _____      h  0.136 ×   10 = _____

i  0.185 × 100 = _____      j  4.05  × 100 = _____

k  0.362 × 1000 = _____      l  3.46  × 1000 = _____

m  5.304 × 1000 = _____      n  12.04  × 1000 = _____

Decimals & Percentages

# Converting fractions to decimals and percentages

## Explanation

You have learnt some of the common equivalent fractions, decimals and percentages, such as $\frac{1}{4} = 0.25 = 25\%$ and $\frac{1}{10} = 0.1 = 10\%$. When converting more complex fractions to decimals and percentages, use a written method to divide the numerator (top number) by the denominator (bottom number).

Example $\frac{3}{8} = 3 \div 8 =$

$$8 \overline{)3\ .\ ^{3}0\ ^{6}0\ ^{4}0}^{0\ .\ 3\ 7\ 5}$$

So $\frac{3}{8}$ is equivalent to **0.375** or **37.5**%.

## Activities

1   Convert each fraction to a decimal and then to a percentage.

   **a**  $\frac{5}{8} =$   _____   _____

   **b**  $\frac{7}{8} =$   _____   _____

   **c**  $\frac{1}{8} =$   _____   _____

2   Convert each fraction to a decimal with **three** decimal places (that is, **three** digits after the decimal point) and then write it as a percentage.

   **a**  $\frac{1}{3} =$   _____   _____

   **b**  $\frac{5}{9} =$   _____   _____

   **c**  $\frac{1}{9} =$   _____   _____

   **d**  $\frac{7}{9} =$   _____   _____

3   The answers to activity 2 are known as **recurring decimals**.
   What do you notice about these decimals?

   _____

   _____

# Multiplying decimals mentally

Use your knowledge of times tables to help you answer decimal multiplication questions mentally. Remember to think about whether your answer will be **10**, **100** or **1000** times smaller than the times tables answer.

| | |
|---|---|
| **0.4 × 6** is **10** times smaller than **4 × 6** | **0.4 × 6 = 2.4** |
| **0.04 × 6** is **100** times smaller than **4 × 6** | **0.04 × 6 = 0.24** |
| **0.4 × 0.6** is **100** times smaller than **4 × 6** | **0.4 × 0.6 = 0.24** |
| **0.04 × 0.6** is **1000** times smaller than **4 × 6** | **0.04 × 0.6 = 0.024** |

As a check, count the number of digits after the decimal point in the question and check that you have the same number of digits after the decimal point in your answer.

Example  $0.4 \times 0.2 = 0.08$          $0.04 \times 0.6 = 0.024$

## Activities

**1**  Answer these questions mentally.

a  0.3  × 3   = _____

b  0.03 × 3   = _____

c  0.02 × 4   = _____

d  0.3  × 5   = _____

e  0.07 × 2   = _____

f  0.04 × 4   = _____

g  0.6  × 8   = _____

h  0.09 × 5   = _____

i  0.7  × 5   = _____

j  0.08 × 3   = _____

k  0.9  × 0.9 = _____

l  0.06 × 0.8 = _____

When the times tables fact results in a multiple of **10**, you don't need to write the last zero on the decimal, but it should still count as one of the digits of the answer when checking.

Example  $0.8 \times 0.5 = 0.40 = 0.4$          $0.04 \times 0.5 = 0.020 = 0.02$

**2**  Answer these questions mentally, but be careful.

a  0.2 × 5   = _____

b  0.06 × 5   = _____

c  0.5 × 0.4 = _____

d  0.05 × 0.8 = _____

# Dividing decimals by whole numbers

## Explanation

When dividing decimals by whole numbers, you can use your knowledge of division to help you. Think of the related division fact and compare this with the decimal. Work out whether it is **10**, **100** or **1000** times smaller, then change your answer so that it is also **10**, **100** or **1000** times smaller.

**Example**

| Question | Related division fact | Calculation |
|---|---|---|
| $3.5 \div 7$ | $35 \div 7 = 5$ | **3.5** is **10** times smaller than **35** so the answer will be **10** times smaller than **5**. $3.5 \div 7 = 0.5$ |
| $0.72 \div 9$ | $72 \div 9 = 8$ | **0.72** is **100** times smaller than **72** so the answer will be **100** times smaller than **8**. $0.72 \div 9 = 0.08$ |

## Activities

**1** Answer these questions mentally.

| Question | Related division fact | | Final answer |
|---|---|---|---|
| **a** $0.24 \div 3$ | _____ | $0.24 \div 3 =$ | _____ |
| **b** $4.5 \div 9$ | _____ | $4.5 \div 9 =$ | _____ |
| **c** $6.4 \div 8$ | _____ | $6.4 \div 8 =$ | _____ |
| **d** $0.08 \div 4$ | _____ | $0.08 \div 4 =$ | _____ |
| **e** $0.84 \div 7$ | _____ | $0.84 \div 7 =$ | _____ |

**2** Answer these questions mentally.

**a** $0.21 \div 3 =$ _____     **b** $2.7 \div 3 =$ _____

**c** $1.6 \div 4 =$ _____     **d** $0.40 \div 5 =$ _____

**e** $0.36 \div 6 =$ _____     **f** $4.2 \div 7 =$ _____

**3** Solve these problems.

**a** What is £**0.48** shared among **six** people? _____

**b** What is **5.6**m split into **eight** equal lengths? _____

# Rounding recurring decimals

## Explanation

Recurring decimals were introduced at the end of page 37. These are decimals where some or all of the digits after the decimal point go on repeating for ever, such as **0.3333333333…**, **0.6666666666…** and **0.16666666666**.

When an answer is a recurring decimal you can show this by writing a dot above each of the repeated digits.

Example  0.3̇    0.6̇    0.16̇    0.3̇75̇

Sometimes you are asked to round the decimals to a given number of decimal places (digits after the decimal point). This is sometimes shortened to 'dps'.

0.333333333333… to **two** dps is **0.33**

0.375375375375… to **two** dps is **0.38**    Remember to round up if you need to.

0.166666666666… to **three** dps is **0.167**

## Activities

**1**  Round each of these recurring decimals to **two** dps.

  **a**  0.4444444…  _____        **b**  0.77777777…  _____

  **c**  0.2525252…  _____        **d**  0.18181818…  _____

  **e**  0.5555555…  _____        **f**  0.67167167…  _____

  **g**  0.5959595…  _____        **h**  0.11111111…  _____

  **i**  0.2752752…  _____        **j**  0.38383838…  _____

**2**  Use a calculator to solve these, rounding your answers.

  **a**  Sanvi has **2**kg of sand which she wants to put equally into three buckets. What is the mass of sand she should put in each bucket? Give your answer to **three** decimal places.  _____

  **b**  Erin has just over £**50**, which she wants to share equally among nine people. How much should she give to each person? Give your answer to **two** decimal places.  _____

# Final test

**1** Draw a ring around the **tenths** digit and underline the **hundredths** digit in these numbers.

   **a** 9.67         **b** 8.629        **c** 15.307       **d** 124.58

**2** What is the **green** digit worth in each of these numbers?

   **a** 7.5 4        **b** 3 2.9 3      **c** 5 8.2 6 8     **d** 2 1 6.2 4 5

   _____      _____     _____     _____

**3** Put these decimals in order of size, **smallest** first.

   **a** 0.3, 0.23, 0.34, 0.29     _____

   **b** 0.67m, 0.54m, 0.6m, 0.59m    _____

**4** Mark these numbers with arrows on the number lines.

   **a** 0.6, 2.4, 1.7, 2.7

              0           1           2           3

   **b** 5.4, 3.7, 4.1, 3.2

              3           4           5           6

**5** Round these numbers to the nearest whole numbers.

   **a** 4.5 → ☐       **b** 7.51 → ☐       **c** 36.302 → ☐

**6** Join pairs of decimals and fractions with the same value.

   $\frac{1}{4}$     0.7     $\frac{1}{5}$     0.9     0.25     $\frac{7}{10}$     0.2

**7** Without a calculator find **75**% of:

a  24 → [   ]    b  60 → [   ]    c  300 → [   ]    d  124 → [   ]

**8** Without a calculator find **70**% of:

a  £200 → [   ]    b  300kg → [   ]    c  20m → [   ]    d  120 → [   ]

**9** Without a calculator find **15**% of:

a  £30 → [   ]    b  80km → [   ]    c  400cm → [   ]    d  160g → [   ]

**10** Complete this table. Write the fractions in their simplest form.

| Percentage | Decimal | Fraction |
|---|---|---|
| 30% | | |
| | 0.7 | |
| | | $\frac{1}{10}$ |

| Percentage | Decimal | Fraction |
|---|---|---|
| 40% | | |
| | 0.8 | |
| | | $\frac{3}{5}$ |

**11** Change these percentages into decimals.

a  15% → [   ]    b  49% → [   ]    c  6% → [   ]    d  78% → [   ]

**12** Change these decimals into percentages.

a  0.32 → [   ]    b  0.4 → [   ]    c  0.07 → [   ]    d  0.51 → [   ]

**13** Change these percentages into fractions in their simplest form.

a  39% → [   ]    b  16% → [   ]    c  2% → [   ]    d  65% → [   ]

**14** Change these fractions into percentages.

a $\frac{7}{10}$ → [ ]  b $\frac{6}{25}$ → [ ]  c $\frac{45}{50}$ → [ ]  d $\frac{19}{20}$ → [ ]

**15** Round these numbers to the nearest tenth.

a [ 4.57 ] → [ ]  b [ 5.49 ] → [ ]  c [ 36.95 ] → [ ]

**16** Draw a ring around the **thousandths** digit in these numbers.

a 8.459  b 31.437  c 12.0298  d 1024.4581

**17** Use a calculator to find these percentages. Approximate first.

a **58**% of **80** = _____  b **12**% of **£72** = _____  c **84**% of **168**m = _____

**18** Without using a calculator, answer these questions.

a  2 7 . 6
  + 5 8 . 2
  ‾‾‾‾‾‾‾

b  6 5 . 4
  + 5 8 . 8
  ‾‾‾‾‾‾‾

c  7 6 . 7
  − 4 9 . 3
  ‾‾‾‾‾‾‾

d  8 3 . 4 1
  − 6 4 . 6 2
  ‾‾‾‾‾‾‾‾

**19** Without using a calculator, answer these questions.

a  38.5 + 19.16 = _____   b  125.45 + 67.8 = _____

c  235.18 − 17.9 = _____   d  29.34 − 18.028 = _____

**20** Write these test scores as percentages and then put them in order, starting with the highest.

$\frac{3}{10}$  $\frac{2}{5}$  $\frac{1}{4}$  $\frac{1}{3}$  _____

**21** The school basketball team played **45** games. They won **60**% of them.
How many games did they win?  _____

**22** A school party of **90** children goes to the Edinburgh Castle.
**40**% of them are girls. How many are girls?  _____

**23** Write each answer as a decimal.

a $8 \div 10 =$ _____ 

b $29 \div 100 =$ _____

c $14 \div 1000 =$ _____

d $673 \div 1000 =$ _____

e $0.06 \times 10 =$ _____

f $0.007 \times 10 =$ _____

g $0.09 \times 100 =$ _____

h $0.015 \times 1000 =$ _____

**24** Convert this fraction to a decimal, and then to a percentage with **one** dps.

$\frac{2}{3} =$ _____ _____

**25** Convert this fraction to a decimal with **three** dps, and then write it as a percentage.

$\frac{2}{11} =$ _____ _____

**26** Answer these questions mentally.

a $0.3 \times 9 =$ _____

b $0.06 \times 3 =$ _____

c $0.02 \times 7 =$ _____

d $0.4 \times 5 =$ _____

e $0.35 \div 5 =$ _____

f $4.8 \div 8 =$ _____

**27** Round each of these recurring decimals to **two** dps.

a $0.6666666\ldots$ _____

b $0.42424242\ldots$ _____

c $0.7657657\ldots$ _____

d $0.85858585\ldots$ _____

**28** Use a calculator to solve this, rounding your answer.

Max has **8** litres of water which he wants to put equally into three containers. How much water should he put in each container?

Give your answer to **three** dps. _____

# Answers to Activities

## Page 5: Decimal tenths and hundredths

**1**  **a** 2.⑥  **b** 6.③  **c** 7.⑨
  **d** 13.⑥  **e** 28.①  **f** 56.④
  **g** 8.⑤4  **h** 9.⑤6  **i** 23.6③

**2**  **a** 2.7②  **b** 5.4③  **c** 9.0②
  **d** 27.5①  **e** 65.9⑦  **f** 128.4⑥
  **g** 5.4⑨2  **h** 8.0⑦2  **i** 19.6⓪8

**3**  **a** 6 hundredths or 0.06
  **b** 4 tenths or 0.4
  **c** 9 tenths or 0.9
  **d** 4 hundredths or 0.04
  **e** 8 tenths or 0.8
  **f** 4 hundredths or 0.04

## Page 6: Writing decimals

**1**  **a** 0.4  **b** 0.8  **c** 0.03
  **d** 0.06  **e** 0.22  **f** 0.96

**2**  **a** 0.7  **b** 0.5  **c** 0.02
  **d** 0.09  **e** 0.47  **f** 0.75

## Page 7: Dividing whole numbers by 10 and 100

**1**  **a** 0.6  **b** 0.8  **c** 1.3
  **d** 6.5  **e** 16.4  **f** 73.2

**2**  **a** 0.03  **b** 0.09  **c** 0.43
  **d** 0.75  **e** 6.83  **f** 7.08

**3**  **a** 50.3  **b** 2.61  **c** 4.3  **d** 0.08

## Page 8: Decimals on a number line 1

**1**  **a** 1.2  **b** 1.5  **c** 1.9  **d** 1.6

**2**  **a**

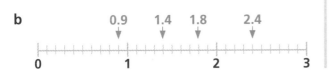

  **b**

## Page 9: Rounding decimals 1

**c**

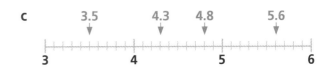

## Page 9: Rounding decimals 1

**1**  **a** 4  **b** 4  **c** 6
  **d** 8  **e** 11  **f** 9
  **g** 19  **h** 26  **i** 74
  **j** 133  **k** 439  **l** 302

## Page 10: Comparing decimals 1

**1**  **a** ⓪.4  0.04  **b** 0.07  ⓪.7
  **c** 0.08  ⓪.8  **d** ⓪.5  0.05
  **e** 0.09  ⓪.9  **f** ⓪.3  0.03

**2**  **a** <  **b** >  **c** >  **d** <
  **e** >  **f** >  **g** <  **h** >
  **i** >  **j** >  **k** <  **l** >

**3**  **a**   **b**

  **c**

## Page 11: Ordering decimals 1

**1**  **a** 0.3, 0.5, 0.6, 0.8
  **b** 0.01, 0.03, 0.07, 0.08
  **c** 0.25, 0.49, 0.53, 0.83
  **d** 0.28, 0.38, 0.82, 0.83
  **e** 0.09, 0.11, 0.62, 0.70
  **f** 0.03, 0.10, 0.13, 0.31

**2**  **a** 0.42kg, 0.4kg, 0.30kg, 0.24kg
  **b** 6.0m, 5.9m, 5.6m, 4.5m
  **c** £9.50, £5.90, £0.59, £0.50

## Page 13: Decimals on a number line 2

**1** a

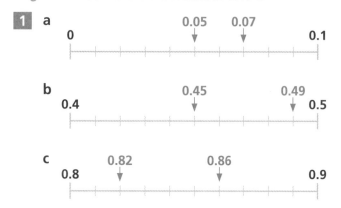

0.05  0.07
0  0.1

b

0.45  0.49
0.4  0.5

c

0.82  0.86
0.8  0.9

**2** a  0.02, 0.09  b  0.11, 0.18
c  0.62, 0.69  d  0.91, 0.98

## Page 14: Rounding decimals 2

**1** a  0  b  1  c  6  d  5  e  8
f  9  g  7  h  4  i  10  j  15

**2** 7.09, 6.72, 6.50

**3** 9.53, 10.43, 9.61

## Page 15: Comparing decimals 2

**1** a  0.6  (0.67)  b  (0.5)  0.48  c  0.77  (0.8)
d  0.6  (0.61)  e  (0.72)  0.7  f  (0.9)  0.89

**2** a

0.26
0.3

b

0.5
0.58

c

2.78
2.8

d

4.79
4.8

e

6.05
6.1

f

7.18
7.2

## Page 16: Ordering decimals 2

**1** a  0.56, 0.8, 0.85, 0.9
b  0.7, 0.75, 0.8, 0.83
c  0.38, 0.39, 0.4, 0.41
d  1.8, 1.86, 1.87, 1.9
e  1.98, 2.0, 2.07, 2.63

**2** a  0.53kg, 0.4kg, 0.31kg, 0.3kg
b  4.3km, 4.25km, 4.2km, 4.17km
c  9.3m, 9.2m, 9.13m, 9.03m
d  3.8kg, 3.78g, 3.7kg, 3.68kg

## Page 17: Rounding decimals 3

**1** a  4.8  b  5.3  c  6.1
d  8.6  e  9.4  f  10.4
g  14.9  h  16.2  i  21.0

**2**

| | Nearest whole number | Nearest tenth | | Nearest whole number | Nearest tenth |
|---|---|---|---|---|---|
| a | 5 | 4.8 | b | 7 | 7.5 |
| c | 13 | 12.8 | d | 23 | 23.4 |
| e | 28 | 27.7 | f | 33 | 32.9 |

## Page 18: Relating decimals to fractions

**1** a  $\frac{1}{4}$  b  $\frac{2}{5}$  c  $\frac{9}{10}$  d  $\frac{1}{2}$

**2**

Start →

| $\frac{1}{6}$ | 0.8 | $\frac{3}{5}$ | 0.5 | $\frac{6}{10}$ | $\frac{1}{10}$ | 0.1 | 0.34 | $\frac{8}{9}$ | 0.1 |
|---|---|---|---|---|---|---|---|---|---|
| $\frac{1}{2}$ | $\frac{1}{5}$ | $\frac{3}{8}$ | $\frac{4}{5}$ | 0.4 | $\frac{2}{5}$ | 0.73 | $\frac{15}{100}$ | 0.76 | 0.63 |
| $\frac{2}{7}$ | 0.5 | 0.1 | 0.3 | 0.2 | $\frac{2}{3}$ | $\frac{3}{7}$ | 0.15 | $\frac{63}{100}$ | $\frac{8}{9}$ |
| 0.12 | $\frac{1}{4}$ | 0.25 | $\frac{3}{10}$ | $\frac{1}{7}$ | $\frac{87}{100}$ | $\frac{3}{5}$ | 0.75 | 0.11 | 0.2 |

→ Finish

# Answers to Activities continued

**Page 19: Decimals with a total of 1**

**1** 13 pairs of decimals adding to 1, in any order

| | |
|---|---|
| 0.7 + 0.3 | 0.22 + 0.78 |
| 0.34 + 0.66 | 0.2 + 0.8 |
| 0.01 + 0.99 | 0.72 + 0.28 |
| 0.92 + 0.08 | 0.9 + 0.1 |
| 0.17 + 0.83 | 0.81 + 0.19 |
| 0.6 + 0.4 | 0.77 + 0.23 |
| 0.51 + 0.49 | 0.65 + 0.35 |

**2** any other pairs that total 1

**Page 20: Adding and subtracting decimals**

**1** a 40.9  b 83.9
c 92.5  d 81.37
e 17.37  f 20.94
g 20.06  h 118.20

**2** a 14.2  b 19.2
c 31.8  d 18.48
e 279.9  f 25.1
g 66.34  h 83.46

**Page 21: Word problems**

**1** a 1.7m  b 6.5cm
c 30km  d 1.1kg
e £12.47  f 0.45l
g 0.95m  h £6.18

**Page 23: Tenths, hundredths and thousandths**

**1** a 3.(9)5  b 4.(3)7  c 8.(9)1
d 0.(5)7  e 15.(0)3  f 38.(1)7
g 78.(0)4  h 10.(3)5

**2** a 3.45(6)  b 5.80(3)
c 11.06(9)  d 8.12(3)
e 35.50(9)1  f 2.90(0)7
g 18.46(2)3  h 2015.23(4)5

**3** a 0.05  b 0.9  c 0.008
d 0.7  e 0.006

**Page 24: Ordering decimals 3**

**1** a 0.24, 0.31, 0.5, 0.7, 0.86
b 0.594, 0.6, 0.65, 0.693, 0.72
c 3.278, 3.3, 3.467, 3.691, 3.72
d 6.007, 6.756, 7.063, 7.1, 7.6

**2** a £6.70, 660p, £6.50, £6.07
b 8.52kg, 6.85kg, 6.58kg, 5.683kg
c 0.45m, 0.42m, 0.348m, 0.3m
d 4.732m, 4.73m, 4.273m, 4.237m

**3** Any combinations between 0.346 and 6.430 ordered correctly are acceptable.

**Page 25: Problems involving thousandths**

**1** a 1.087km  b 0.366m  c 1.292kg
d 0.158kg  e 2.175l  f 0.675l
g 0.211kg

**Page 26: What percentages are**

**1** a 50%  b 80%  c 40%
d 30%  e 40%  f 15%

**2** a putting their all into it
b one-tenth (10%) is fat
c half price

**Page 27: Estimating percentages**

**1** 50%, 95%, 10%, 65%, 5%

**2** 50%, 20%, 35%, 80%, 75%

**3** a 60%  b 50%  c 5%  d 10%  e 80%

**Page 29: Finding percentages mentally 1**

**1** a 9  b 12  c 15  d 36
e 48  f 75  g 300  h 600

**2** a 2  b 4  c 20  d 12
e 15  f 25  g 50  h 220

**3** a 3  b 9  c 36  d 48
e 39  f 120  g 270  h 750

Schofield & Sims | Understanding Maths

47

## Page 30: Finding percentages mentally 2

**1**    **a** £16      **b** 28g      **c** 168m

**2**    **a** £32      **b** 100kg      **c** 360m

**3**    **a** £42      **b** 480km      **c** 72cm

**4**    **a** £9      **b** 27km      **c** 30cm

**5**    **a** £140      **b** 7km      **c** 175cm

## Page 31: Relating percentages to decimals and fractions 1

**1**

| Percentage | Decimal | Fraction | Percentage | Decimal | Fraction |
|---|---|---|---|---|---|
| **50%** | 0.5 | $\frac{1}{2}$ | **80%** | 0.8 | $\frac{4}{5}$ |
| **40%** | 0.4 | $\frac{2}{5}$ | 30% | **0.3** | $\frac{3}{10}$ |
| 10% | **0.1** | $\frac{1}{10}$ | 20% | 0.2 | $\frac{1}{5}$ |
| 60% | **0.6** | $\frac{3}{5}$ | 90% | **0.9** | $\frac{9}{10}$ |
| 70% | 0.7 | $\frac{7}{10}$ | 1% | **0.01** | $\frac{1}{100}$ |

**2**    **a** $\frac{2}{5}$      **b** $\frac{7}{5}$      **c** 0.25      **d** 0.95

## Page 32: Relating percentages to decimals and fractions 2

**1**    **a** 0.32      **b** 0.27      **c** 0.63
       **d** 0.09      **e** 0.01      **f** 1.00

**2**    **a** 72%      **b** 45%      **c** 87%
       **d** 30%      **e** 60%      **f** 2%

**3**    **a** $\frac{49}{100}$      **b** $\frac{3}{20}$      **c** $\frac{21}{25}$
       **d** $\frac{1}{20}$      **e** $\frac{1}{100}$      **f** $\frac{3}{4}$

**4**    **a** 30%      **b** 90%      **c** 80%
       **d** 5%      **e** 12%      **f** 34%

## Page 33: Percentage problems

**1**    **a** 90%, 84%, 80%
       **b** 50%, 40%, 30%
       **c** 30%, 25%, 20%

**2**    **a** 9      **b** 32      **c** 51      **d** 3

## Page 34: Finding percentages with a calculator

**1**    **a** £76.80      **b** £15.36
       **c** £42.68      **d** 29.40kg
       **e** 120.96kg      **f** 8.05kg
       **g** 29.58ml      **h** 145ml
       **i** 250.10ml      **j** 287.10m
       **k** 42.48m      **l** 132.48m

**2**    **a** £9.45      **b** £11.20      **c** £39.33
       **d** £13.80      **e** £33.60      **f** £23.40

## Page 36: Multiplying and dividing numbers by 10, 100 and 1000

**1**    **a** 0.4      **b** 2.9
       **c** 0.04      **d** 0.29
       **e** 0.004      **f** 0.029

**2**    **a** 0.6      **b** 0.06
       **c** 7      **d** 1.5
       **e** 6      **f** 46
       **g** 1.2      **h** 1.36
       **i** 18.5      **j** 405
       **k** 362      **l** 3460
       **m** 5304      **n** 12 040

## Page 37: Converting fractions to decimals and percentages

**1**    **a** 0.625, 62.5%
       **b** 0.875, 87.5%
       **c** 0.125, 12.5%

**2**    **a** 0.333, 33.3%
       **b** 0.556, 55.6%
       **c** 0.111, 11.1%
       **d** 0.778, 77.8%

**3**    The digits keep repeating.

## Page 38: Multiplying decimals mentally

**1**
| | |
|---|---|
| **a** 0.9 | **b** 0.09 |
| **c** 0.08 | **d** 1.5 |
| **e** 0.14 | **f** 0.16 |
| **g** 4.8 | **h** 0.45 |
| **i** 3.5 | **j** 0.24 |
| **k** 0.81 | **l** 0.048 |

**2**
| | |
|---|---|
| **a** 1 or 1.0 | **b** 0.3 or 0.30 |
| **c** 0.2 or 0.20 | **d** 0.04 or 0.040 |

## Page 39: Dividing decimals by whole numbers

**1**
**a** 24 ÷ 3 = 8      0.08
**b** 45 ÷ 9 = 5      0.5
**c** 64 ÷ 8 = 8      0.8
**d** 8 ÷ 4 = 2      0.02
**e** 84 ÷ 7 = 12      0.12

**2**
| | | |
|---|---|---|
| **a** 0.07 | **b** 0.9 | **c** 0.4 |
| **d** 0.08 | **e** 0.06 | **f** 0.6 |

**3**
| | |
|---|---|
| **a** £0.08 | **b** 0.7m |

## Page 40: Rounding recurring decimals

**1**
| | |
|---|---|
| **a** 0.44 | **b** 0.78 |
| **c** 0.25 | **d** 0.18 |
| **e** 0.56 | **f** 0.67 |
| **g** 0.60 | **h** 0.11 |
| **i** 0.28 | **j** 0.38 |

**2**
**a** 0.667kg
**b** £5.56

# Answers to Progress tests

## PROGRESS TEST 1 – Page 12

**1**  a  7.⑥  **b**  3.③8
  c  17.⑨5  **d**  24.⓪25

**2**  a  4.7⑥  **b**  154.7③
  c  94.7①2  **d**  20.0②4

**3**  a  9 hundredths or 0.09
  b  4 tenths or 0.4
  c  1 hundredth or 0.01

**4**  a  5.3  **b**  0.08  **c**  0.42

**5**  a  <  **b**  >  **c**  >

**6**  a  0.1, 0.3, 0.6, 0.9
  b  0.05, 0.57, 0.75, 0.77

**7**  a

| 0.4 | 0.9 | 1.3 | 1.8 |

```
|++++++++++|++++++++++|
0          1          2
```

  b

| 0.7 | 1.3 | 1.9 2.1 |

```
|++++++++++|++++++++++|++++++++++|
0          1          2          3
```

**8**  a  4  **b**  74  **c**  29

## PROGRESS TEST 2 – Page 22

**1**  a  0.01, 0.07
  b  0.52, 0.55

**2**  a  9  **b**  7  **c**  15

**3**  a  0.5  **b**  4.5  **c**  12.8

**4**  a ⓪.③ 0.29  **b**  0.7 ⓪.⑦⑨  **c** ⓪.⑨ 0.10

**5**  a  0.59, 0.63, 0.66, 0.7
  b  0.1, 0.18, 0.2, 0.81
  c  0.49m, 0.5m, 0.58m, 0.61m

**6**  $\frac{3}{4} = 0.75$

  $0.3 = \frac{3}{10}$

  $\frac{4}{5} = 0.8$

**7**  a  43.2  **b**  50.52
  c  125.25  **d**  44.37

## PROGRESS TEST 3 – Page 28

**1**  a  8.45⑨  **b**  31.43⑦
  c  12.02⑨8  **d**  1024.45⑧1

**2**  a  0.403
  b  1.029

**3**  a  0.045, 0.05, 0.4, 0.405
  b  0.008, 0.03, 0.032, 0.04
  c  3.573, 3.58, 3.59, 3.6

**4**  1.252m

**5**  a  50%  **b**  30%  **c**  35%

**6**  30%, 75%, 10%, 95%, 0%

## PROGRESS TEST 4 – Page 35

**1**  a  24  **b**  46  **c**  90

**2**  a  6  **b**  15  **c**  30

**3**  a  6  **b**  27  **c**  300

**4**  a  £60  **b**  45kg  **c**  93m

**5**  a  £27  **b**  90km  **c**  225cm

**6**

| Percentage | Decimal | Fraction | Percentage | Decimal | Fraction |
|---|---|---|---|---|---|
| **70%** | 0.7 | $\frac{7}{10}$ | **20%** | 0.2 | $\frac{1}{5}$ |
| 40% | **0.4** | $\frac{2}{5}$ | 50% | **0.5** | $\frac{1}{2}$ |
| 30% | 0.3 | $\frac{3}{10}$ | 80% | 0.8 | $\frac{4}{5}$ |

**7**  a  $\frac{4}{5} = 80\%$, $\frac{3}{4} = 75\%$ so $\frac{4}{5}$ is greater
  b  25

# Answers to Final test

**1**  **a**  9.6̲7̲   **b**  8.6̲2̲9
**c**  15.3̲0̲7   **d**  124.5̲8̲

**2**  **a**  0.04 or 4 hundredths
**b**  0.9 or 9 tenths
**c**  0.06 or 6 hundredths
**d**  0.04 or 4 hundredths

**3**  **a**  0.23, 0.29, 0.3, 0.34
**b**  0.54m, 0.59m, 0.6m, 0.67m

**4**  **a**
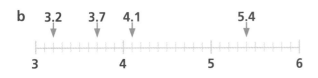

**b**

**5**  **a**  5   **b**  8   **c**  36

**6**  $\frac{1}{4} = 0.25$, $0.7 = \frac{7}{10}$, $\frac{1}{5} = 0.2$

**7**  **a**  18   **b**  45   **c**  225   **d**  93

**8**  **a**  £140   **b**  210kg   **c**  14m   **d**  84

**9**  **a**  £4.50   **b**  12km   **c**  60cm   **d**  24g

**10**

| Percentage | Decimal | Fraction | Percentage | Decimal | Fraction |
|---|---|---|---|---|---|
| **30%** | 0.3 | $\frac{3}{10}$ | **40%** | 0.4 | $\frac{2}{5}$ |
| 70% | **0.7** | $\frac{7}{10}$ | 80% | **0.8** | $\frac{4}{5}$ |
| 10% | 0.1 | $\frac{1}{10}$ | 60% | 0.6 | $\frac{3}{5}$ |

**11**  **a**  0.15   **b**  0.49   **c**  0.06   **d**  0.78

**12**  **a**  32%   **b**  40%   **c**  7%   **d**  51%

**13**  **a**  $\frac{39}{100}$   **b**  $\frac{4}{25}$   **c**  $\frac{1}{50}$   **d**  $\frac{13}{20}$

**14**  **a**  70%   **b**  24%   **c**  90%   **d**  95%

**15**  **a**  4.6   **b**  5.5   **c**  37.0

**16**  **a**  8.45̲9̲   **b**  31.43̲7̲
**c**  12.02̲9̲8   **d**  1024.45̲8̲1

**17**  **a**  46.4   **b**  £8.64   **c**  141.12m

**18**  **a**  85.8   **b**  124.2   **c**  27.4   **d**  18.79

**19**  **a**  57.66   **b**  193.25
**c**  217.28   **d**  11.312

**20**  40%, 33.3%, 30%, 25%

**21**  27

**22**  36

**23**  **a**  0.8   **b**  0.29
**c**  0.014   **d**  0.673
**e**  0.6   **f**  0.07
**g**  9   **h**  15

**24**  0.66666… = 66.7%

**25**  0.182 = 18.2%

**26**  **a**  2.7   **b**  0.18
**c**  0.14   **d**  2
**e**  0.07   **f**  0.6

**27**  **a**  0.67   **b**  0.42   **c**  0.77   **d**  0.86

**28**  2.667l